# TEACH

# STAY

# LOVE

## A Reflective Journal
## to Help You Stay
## In the Profession You Love

Printed in the United States of America

First Printing, 2017

ISBN-13 978-0-9986219-0-6

Disturb the Universe, LLC

# PSST...HEY. YOU. YEAH. YOU! SO...SOMEONE TOLD ME YOU'RE A TEACHER. IS THAT TRUE? YOU'RE A FOR REAL, CAPE ON YOUR BACK, "S" ON YOUR CHEST, CHAMPION OF CHILDREN? YOU ARE SO

# AWESOME!

No, seriously. You are. Yeah. I know. It doesn't always FEEL that way but trust me, when I say:

### You. Are. A. Rockstar.

So, you may ask, if that's so, why do I feel like quitting? At least once a week? Simple. Because you're human. Because you're probably exhausted. Because teaching is hard as heck and sometimes it feels like a thankless job. Because you're in the only profession that's viewed under a microscope daily. Because just when you get used to one mandate someone changes it. Because the mandates have mandates. Because kids won't behave. Because parents won't listen (and sometimes they won't behave either). Because if that administrator comes in your classroom one more time...How am I doin' so far?

Then again, maybe this isn't you. Maybe you aren't tired, or frustrated, or 20 seconds away from walking out of the front door. Maybe you love coming to work every day and your kids are angels and their parents are too. Maybe you take change with ease and you teach like your hair is on fire and each day you wake up you are excited to come to work. Nice picture, right?

Well, whether you are barely holding on by your fingernails or you're floating on the proverbial Cloud 9, you are deeply important to the students that you teach. And if no one has told you lately how amazing you are, you are. None of us chose teaching because we thought it was going to be easy. None of us chose it because we wanted to be rich. None of us chose it because we wanted to be part of a profession that is ruthlessly, and sometimes mercilessly, criticized by everyone from parents to politicians, students to citizens, and members of the community to members of the media. Yet, here we are.

And the reason I believe we are still here is because there is a gene that has yet to be discovered that all teachers share, a gene that made us predisposed to wanting to change the world by educating it's children. See, we didn't **really** choose teaching. It chose us. In some way, we were called to this. Why? Well, that's what this journal is for. So you can remember your why.

*The TeachStayLove Journal* was created to help motivate, inspire, and most of all remind you why you teach, why you stay, and what makes you love what you do. Inside, you will find quotes, stories, action items, points to ponder, and affirmations all created to support you as you journal your way to a place of peace, and if not peace, at least a place of diminished irritation (Baby steps are still steps you know).

The journal is set up into three sections. Want to guess what the sections are called? Yup. Teach. Stay. Love. Each section contains five stand alone quotes and five quotes with stories attached all of which come from someone's very real personal experiences. Mine. Some are humorous, some are serious, most are relatable, and all are transparent. And that is by design. In my 12 years of being an educator, I've learned a thing or five about myself as a person and a thing or six about myself as a teacher and I don't believe any of this wisdom was intended for me to keep hidden. I am of the belief that we don't have experiences just for our benefit. I believe we have them so we can help others.

In addition to each quote and quote/story combination, you have an entire page to journal your thoughts, or doodle, or color, or cuss, or pray or whatever you need. It's your journal so in the words of Ray Charles, make it do what it do.

Lastly, there are thirty quotes, and there is a place on each journal page for a date, but you are in no way obligated to complete the journal in order or at all. Take what you need, when you need it. If that means every day for 30 days, cool. If that means once per week, great. If that means whenever you can get to it, awesome. But at least commit to doing **something** with it, except throwing it across the room or at somebody ...unless that will help. No. Seriously. Don't do that.

I hope you enjoy completing this journal as much as I did making it. Already working on another one that spans 180 days so if you have any suggestions, improvements, or things you'd like to see in the next journal, shoot me an email at: chantrise@disturb-the-universe.com. After all, I'm making it for you. Happy Journaling!

*Chantrise*

Education is the key to success in life and teachers make a lasting impact in the lives of their students.

Solomon Ortiz

# TEACH

# The journey begins wherever you decide to start.

TODAY:_____ _____ _____

I TEACH BECAUSE:

_____

_____

_____

_____

_____

_____

_____

_____

_____

_____

_____

_____

_____

_____

_____

_____

_____

_____

_____

_____

_____

_____

_____

_____

# TEACH

Don't ask for easy.
Ask for strength.

Teaching. Although I used to play "school" with my parents and my stuffed animals, being a teacher was never anything I wanted to be. For one, teachers were always broke, and for two they had to deal with other people's kids all day. I knew first hand how my classmates and I acted and I wanted no part of it. And then I found myself teaching 9th grade. In my 4th year, I was teaching seven classes a day, 35 strong, except for my 1st period which was 42. Yup. 42 9th graders first thing in the morning. After a particularly expletive worthy day, I went to my principal to ask if some of my classes could be reduced. "Nope," he said. "We don't have anywhere else to put them." I just looked at him and said, "So you want me to quit? You must because I can't do this every day." He looked up from what he was working on and said, "You didn't get into teaching because it was easy, right? So, stop looking for easy. Start digging deep and find your strength."

Look. We didn't choose this profession because it was going to be all unicorns and bunny rabbits. We chose it because we believed we could make a difference, and doing that isn't ever easy, but it sure is worth it.

Point to Ponder: Where can you find some strength?

TODAY:_____ _____ _____

I TEACH BECAUSE:

_____
_____
_____
_____
_____
_____
_____
_____
_____
_____
_____
_____
_____
_____
_____
_____
_____
_____
_____
_____
_____
_____
_____
_____
_____

"We" accomplishes much more than just "I."

TODAY:_____  _____  _____

I TEACH BECAUSE:

_____

_____

_____

_____

_____

_____

_____

_____

_____

_____

_____

_____

_____

_____

_____

_____

_____

_____

_____

_____

_____

_____

_____

_____

# TEACH

It's not your mistakes
that define you.
It's how you recover from them.

One of the first things you'll discover about teaching, if you haven't already, is that at some point, no matter how amazing you are, you're going to mess up. Yup. You're going to make a mistake and it's going to feel like the world has ended. But guess what? It probably won't. While mistakes suck, they can only define you if a) you don't learn from them or b) you make them again...and again...and again.

It's how you respond AFTER you make the mistake that truly shows who you are as a teacher and as a person. So, don't bask in the blunder! Own it. Learn from it. Move on.

Point to Ponder: Think of a mistake you made and what lesson you learned from it. How can you ensure you don't make the same mistake again?

TODAY:_____  _____  _____

I TEACH BECAUSE:

_____

_____

_____

_____

_____

_____

_____

_____

_____

_____

_____

_____

_____

_____

_____

_____

_____

_____

_____

_____

_____

_____

_____

_____

# TEACH

Those aren't buterflies in your stomach. That's destiny calling. Answer.

TODAY:_____ _____ _____

I TEACH BECAUSE:

_____
_____
_____
_____
_____
_____
_____
_____
_____
_____
_____
_____
_____
_____
_____
_____
_____
_____
_____
_____
_____
_____
_____
_____
_____
_____

# TEACH

## Doing less is sometimes the best part of the lesson.

As teachers, we are often expected, or required, to teach like our hair is on fire and while that makes for a great show, sometimes less is truly more. No matter what anyone has told you, you can't be "on" all the time. Sometimes, your students need to be the sages on the stages!

If you are unfamiliar with the "gradual release model" of instruction run, don't walk, to your nearest search engine and look it up. What you will discover is a method of teaching that frees you up to act as facilitator for your students as they make meaning of the lesson and acquire knowledge for themselves. That makes your work less and their work more. Now how cool is that?

Action Item: Hit up your favorite search engine and search for "Gradual Release Model." The Teaching Channel has a 5 minute video that gives a great overview. Then, choose a lesson where you can try it out.

TODAY:_____  _____  _____

I TEACH BECAUSE:

_____
_____
_____
_____
_____
_____
_____
_____
_____
_____
_____
_____
_____
_____
_____
_____
_____
_____
_____
_____
_____
_____
_____

# TEACH

Awesomeness doesn't require perfection. It requires commitment.

TODAY:_____ _____ _____

I TEACH BECAUSE:

_____
_____
_____
_____
_____
_____
_____
_____
_____
_____
_____
_____
_____
_____
_____
_____
_____
_____
_____
_____
_____
_____
_____
_____
_____

# TEACH

## Look beyond the obvious. The answer you seek may be hiding in plain sight.

Long ago and in a galaxy not so far away, I had a student named Texas. No. That wasn't his real name but it fit the size of his attitude. Texas used to skip my class every day and when I was actually able to get him to class he did nothing. Clearly, he just wasn't a good student. That is until one day, as I was giving notes, I finally noticed he was writing something down. Excited that he was paying attention, I walked over to commend him for his efforts and discovered he wasn't taking notes. He was writing song lyrics. I immediately became irritated until I actually read what he had written and it was outstanding. From that day forth we had a deal: He'd take notes for the first 40 minutes of class and I would allow him to write for the last 10. Problem solved. After that, we had no more issues and he graduated with college acceptances and scholarships...on time. Sometimes, the answer you're looking for is staring you right in the face. All you have to do is pay attention.

Point to Ponder: What discoveries could you make about your students if you just looked beyond the obvious?

TODAY:_____ _____ _____

I TEACH BECAUSE:

_____
_____
_____
_____
_____
_____
_____
_____
_____
_____
_____
_____
_____
_____
_____
_____
_____
_____
_____
_____
_____
_____
_____
_____
_____
_____

# TEACH

# Disturb the Universe

TODAY:_____ _____ _____

I TEACH BECAUSE:

_____
_____
_____
_____
_____
_____
_____
_____
_____
_____
_____
_____
_____
_____
_____
_____
_____
_____
_____
_____
_____
_____
_____
_____
_____

# TEACH

Failure is temporary. Defeat is permanent. One means falling and choosing to get up. The other means falling and chosing not to.

Teenagers are invincible. Well, at least they think they are and they live life with this premise firmly attached to their non-existent frontal lobes. But, we know differently and inevitably, we are faced with the broken spirit of a child who has learned the truth. So, what's a teacher to do?

The best way to support a student who is convinced the sky has fallen as a result of failure is to reassure them that the sky has not fallen and how they respond greatly determines if they fail again (Sound familiar?). As annoying as they can be, teenagers, above all else, are people first and just like us, they need to know they can recover. So tell them they can and then show them how.

Action Item: Think of a time when you failed and share it with a student who needs some encouragement.

TODAY:_____ _____ _____

I TEACH BECAUSE:

_____

_____

_____

_____

_____

_____

_____

_____

_____

_____

_____

_____

_____

_____

_____

_____

_____

_____

_____

_____

_____

_____

_____

Don't teach because that's all you can do. Teach because it's your calling. And once you realize that, you have a responsibility to the young people.

Maya Angelou

# STAY

# STAY

The school can't run without YOU!

TODAY:_____  _____  _____

I STAY BECAUSE:

_____
_____
_____
_____
_____
_____
_____
_____
_____
_____
_____
_____
_____
_____
_____
_____
_____
_____
_____
_____
_____
_____
_____
_____
_____
_____

# STAY

## Sometimes what looks like a mess is really a smudge. Look again.

Ever meet a person who puts the "over" in "over exaggeration?" You know, that person who, on a scale of 1-10, will take a 2 situation and turn it into a 12? I'm not saying this is me but there have been occasions, especially around evaluation time, when something goes wrong and I start thinking about where I'm going to find enough boxes to pack up my room. Newsflash: I've been teaching for over a decade and all of the situations I thought were 12s turned out to be just 2s, or at least they weren't as bad as I thought.

Look. Whether you want to admit it or not, teaching can be down right, nerve wreckingly, adult beverage worthy and when you're being observed it can be that times two or three. That's why it's really easy to climb the proverbial mountain that really is just a molehill. So, before you find yourself crying in a closet (What? You've never cried in a closet before?), pause and get some perspective. If you can't, find someone who can.

Point to Ponder: What's one situation you thought was far more serious than it was? How can you keep yourself from blowing small things out of proportion?

TODAY:_____  _____  _____

I STAY BECAUSE:

_____
_____
_____
_____
_____
_____
_____
_____
_____
_____
_____
_____
_____
_____
_____
_____
_____
_____
_____
_____
_____
_____
_____
_____
_____

# STAY

Watch and listen twice as much as you speak. Not everything that is seen and heard needs to be spoken.

TODAY:_____  _____  _____

I STAY BECAUSE:

_____
_____
_____
_____
_____
_____
_____
_____
_____
_____
_____
_____
_____
_____
_____
_____
_____
_____
_____
_____
_____
_____
_____
_____
_____

# STAY

## Everyone's not going to be excited about your elevation. Elevate anyway.

Sometimes working in a school is the equivalent of being in the movie Mean Girls. There are cliques, and gossip, and people who are just downright nasty. Add to that your haters and it can feel like your worst high school nightmare come to life. But, in the face of such circumstances, your job isn't to succumb to the negativity. Nope. YOUR job is to be great in spite of what is going on around you. Let the cliques click, let the gossipers gossip, let the nasty folk be nasty, and let the haters hate on because, at the end of the day, what they think shouldn't affect your awesomeness. And no doubt about it. You. Are. Awesome. If you weren't why would they be so upset? Exactly. They wouldn't. So stand up, adjust your crown, and give them something to hate you for.

Affirmation: Say the following, "I was born awesome. I am currently awesome. I will continue to BE awesome. No matter what!"

TODAY:_____  _____  _____

I STAY BECAUSE:

_____
_____
_____
_____
_____
_____
_____
_____
_____
_____
_____
_____
_____
_____
_____
_____
_____
_____
_____
_____
_____
_____
_____
_____
_____
_____

# STAY

# Live.

# Learn.

# Grow.

TODAY:_____ _____ _____

I STAY BECAUSE:

_____
_____
_____
_____
_____
_____
_____
_____
_____
_____
_____
_____
_____
_____
_____
_____
_____
_____
_____
_____
_____
_____
_____

# STAY

## Remember, you stand on the shoulders of giants and walk in the footsteps of greatness.

Mr. Peter Capidolupo was my 10th grade English teacher and was, and still is, my most favorite. Long before "student engagement" was the phrase du jour, he was the one teacher who made learning fun. On the very first day of class, he leapt on his desk and began to recite a monologue from one of Shakespeare's plays. I was hooked. When I started teaching, I thought long about the type of teacher I wanted to be and Mr. Capidolupo was my first, and only, choice. I wanted students to love coming to my class the way I loved going to his. I wanted to inspire and challenge and engage my students the way he did me. I wanted to be the teacher my students never forgot. I am who I am today because he was who he was yesterday. Yes. Teaching can feel lonely and thankless sometimes but I promise, if you use your memory, you'll discover you are not alone.

Point to Ponder: Who's the one person, or people, who inspire you the most? How can you use them to keep you strong when things get rough?

TODAY:_____  _____  _____

I STAY BECAUSE:

_____
_____
_____
_____
_____
_____
_____
_____
_____
_____
_____
_____
_____
_____
_____
_____
_____
_____
_____
_____
_____
_____
_____
_____
_____

# STAY

Sometimes all it takes is some good theme music to make everything better.

TODAY:_____ _____ _____

I STAY BECAUSE:

_____
_____
_____
_____
_____
_____
_____
_____
_____
_____
_____
_____
_____
_____
_____
_____
_____
_____
_____
_____
_____
_____
_____
_____
_____

# STAY

## Know and understand your faults and operate in excellence anyway.

Okay. Confession time. I am a procrastinator. Yup. I was that kid who waited until the last minute to do everything and I am only a slightly taller version of that kid today. But, I am also a perfectionist which means, when faced with a deadline, I'm stressed out because I should've started earlier but I can't go to bed until it's just right #TeamNoSleep. I've tried to change but so far nothing has worked. So what do I do? Admit I'm a procrastinator, admit I'm a perfectionist, buy lots of coffee, and get stuff done. Being "Last Minute Lucy" is no excuse for me to be mediocre. I believe in being amazing so I work around my flaw. Whatever fault you have doesn't give you the right to give anything less than your best. You were created to be great so be that. No excuses.

Action Item: Think about that one fault that could potentially get in the way of your greatness. Come up with a plan to either fix it or work around it.

TODAY:_____ _____ _____

I STAY BECAUSE:

_____
_____
_____
_____
_____
_____
_____
_____
_____
_____
_____
_____
_____
_____
_____
_____
_____
_____
_____
_____
_____
_____
_____

# STAY

People buy
what they
believe in.
Who's buying
into you?

TODAY:_____ _____ _____

I STAY BECAUSE:

_____

_____

_____

_____

_____

_____

_____

_____

_____

_____

_____

_____

_____

_____

_____

_____

_____

_____

# STAY

## If you're tired of someone beating a dead horse, get a new horse.

My father is the king of overkill. There has never been a point, opinion, or judgment he didnt feel comfortable bringing up...repeatedly. "Leave well enough alone" is not a statement with which he is remotely familiar. But, while eye-rollingly annoying most times, his inclination for repetition taught me one very important lesson: If you're tired of someone harping on the same point, do something different so they'll stop.

One of the most frequent complaints I hear from teachers is that one administrator or another keeps bringing up the same issue in their evaluations. "I don't know what he wants!" My response: "Have you asked?" Sometimes the fix to the problem is as simple as asking a question (This goes for situations outside of school too by the way). Stop getting frustrated and irritated over an issue that can easily be solved with just a little bit of old fashioned communication.

Point to Ponder: What is one issue, situation, pain in the butt problem in your life that you wish people would just stop talking about? What can you do to help them find a new horse?

TODAY:_____ _____ _____

I STAY BECAUSE:

_____

_____

_____

_____

_____

_____

_____

_____

_____

_____

_____

_____

_____

_____

_____

_____

_____

_____

_____

_____

_____

_____

_____

_____

_____

Teachers have three loves: love of learning, love of learners, and the love of bringing the first two loves together.

Scott Hayden

# LOVE

# LOVE

Because sometimes "because" is the only reason you need.

TODAY:_____ _____ _____

I LOVE BECAUSE:

_____
_____
_____
_____
_____
_____
_____
_____
_____
_____
_____
_____
_____
_____
_____
_____
_____
_____
_____
_____
_____
_____
_____

# LOVE

## Be you and do so unapologetically.

I'm a quirk. My daughter says I'm weird, my father says I'm special, and my mother says I'm just like my father. Any way you slice and/or dice it, I am one unique individual. For years on the first day of school I would wear leopard print Mickey Mouse ears. Why? Why not? I called them my "First Day of School Ears" and over time, students looked forward to seeing me in them (Until they broke. I'm looking for a new pair by the way). They were as much a part of me as my own ears and I liked them. It hasn't always been this way, me being comfortable in my own skin. That took time and the eventual fatigue that came with always trying to fit in.

One of the best gifts we can give our students in an age when people are lauded for "following suit" is to teach them to be different, be unique, be themselves. And how do we do that? By being OURSELVES. We don't live in a George Orwell novel and we are not Borg (Oh. I'm a nerd too). So stop apologizing for bringing pom poms to class or teaching your class dressed as Darth Vader. If being you helps you reach your students, just do it!

Point to Ponder: How can you use what is most unique about you to engage (or further engage) your students?

TODAY:_____  _____  _____

I LOVE BECAUSE:

_____
_____
_____
_____
_____
_____
_____
_____
_____
_____
_____
_____
_____
_____
_____
_____
_____
_____
_____
_____
_____
_____

# LOVE

Empowered teachers face problems in two ways: with their hearts and their heads. Their hearts feel the problem but their heads solve it.

TODAY:_____ _____ _____

I LOVE BECAUSE:

_____
_____
_____
_____
_____
_____
_____
_____
_____
_____
_____
_____
_____
_____
_____
_____
_____
_____
_____
_____
_____
_____
_____
_____
_____

# LOVE

Flowers can still bloom in the desert. Today be grateful for the desert you're in.

A few months ago, I found myself possessing only my last nerve. All my other nerves had been tap danced, plucked, or stood on and I was over all of it. I was ready to walk away from a job and school where I had worked for 12 years. Then I got sick. Very sick. So sick my doctor put me on medical leave for three months. When I called my principal to tell her she said, "Good. You need to rest. We'll take care of everything until you get back" (I know! That's what I said too!). At that moment I realized that had I been anywhere else and gotten sick I would have gotten a very different response. As much as I was ready to leave (so I thought), I immediately became grateful for where I was. I had learned to find the positive in the midst of the negative. In other words, I learned to find the flowers in the midst of the desert. If you look, I bet you can find some too.

Action Item: Every day for a week, find at least one positive thing to focus on. Write each one on a sticky note and post them on your desk as reminders of the flowers you found.

TODAY:_____ _____ _____

I LOVE BECAUSE:

_____
_____
_____
_____
_____
_____
_____
_____
_____
_____
_____
_____
_____
_____
_____
_____
_____
_____
_____
_____
_____
_____
_____
_____
_____
_____
_____

# LOVE

Humble yourself before someone else does.

TODAY:_____  _____  _____

I LOVE BECAUSE:

_____
_____
_____
_____
_____
_____
_____
_____
_____
_____
_____
_____
_____
_____
_____
_____
_____
_____
_____
_____
_____
_____
_____
_____
_____

# LOVE

## Learn to care without carrying. Everyone's burdens aren't yours to bear.

When I became a teacher, my father gave me one piece of advice: "Don't take your students home with you." At the time, I didn't really understand what he meant but it was not long before I figured it out. I am that teacher whose students start off in my class but end up in my heart (Don't believe me? Twenty of them were a part of my wedding. Yes. really). So, because I'm THAT teacher I brought my students problems home with me which quickly became overwhelming and frustrating. I was stressing myself out over situations that, while heartbreaking in most cases, weren't mine to carry.

Part of being a teacher is caring for the students we teach, building relationships that allow us to move beyond whatever issues they bring to school so we can give them what they need to be successful in life. An education. To take care of our kids we must first take care of ourselves so lay the burden down, and get some rest.

Action Item: Say, "Today, I will practice caring for my students without carrying their issues home with me."

TODAY:_____ _____ _____

I LOVE BECAUSE:

_____
_____
_____
_____
_____
_____
_____
_____
_____
_____
_____
_____
_____
_____
_____
_____
_____
_____
_____
_____
_____
_____
_____
_____

# LOVE

Learn to speak when no one else will and listen when no one else is.

TODAY:_____ _____ _____

I LOVE BECAUSE:

_____
_____
_____
_____
_____
_____
_____
_____
_____
_____
_____
_____
_____
_____
_____
_____
_____
_____
_____
_____
_____
_____
_____
_____
_____

# LOVE

## If work doesn't get you the option to push pause, push pause yourself.

In 2006, I was diagnosed with an autoimmune disease called Lupus. What this means is my immune system runs on auto-pilot, atacking my healthy organs as if they were a virus. One of the triggers for what is called a "flare" is stress and lack of sleep. By early 2016, I was teaching and finishing my dissertation so stress and insomnia were both in large supply. But I went to work anyway because, as you probably already know, it requires less work to go TO work than it does to stay home. Well, I found out the hard way what happens when you don't take a break: three months of medical leave. But what makes this really bad isn't that I was out. It's that I had more than enough sick days to BE out. Why? Because for three years I didn't take not one sick day, even when I needed it. Don't be me. The world won't end if you miss a day. It might, however, if you don't.

Action Item: Put in for a mental health day if you need to or commit to finding some time to unwind.

TODAY:_____ _____ _____

I LOVE BECAUSE:

_____

_____

_____

_____

_____

_____

_____

_____

_____

_____

_____

_____

_____

_____

_____

_____

_____

_____

_____

_____

_____

_____

# LOVE

When people laugh behind your back let your success laugh back.

TODAY:_____ _____ _____

I LOVE BECAUSE:

_____
_____
_____
_____
_____
_____
_____
_____
_____
_____
_____
_____
_____
_____
_____
_____
_____
_____
_____
_____
_____
_____
_____
_____

# LOVE

They say creativity is just intelligence having fun. How much fun has yours had lately?

The story goes that one day a professor drew a squiggly blob on the board and asked his students what it was. "A blob," they responded. He then went on to tell them that he asked the same question to a group of 3rd graders and their responses were, "a squished bug," "the eye of a dinosaur who needs glasses," and "black spaghetti." He then asked the students why they thought the responses were so different and one answered, "because we are more educated." The professor responded, "And that's the problem."

Research shows that students stop liking school when they no longer have the opportunity to flex their creativity. It's the old, "all work and no play makes [insert name] a dull person." You know who else that is true for? Adults, teachers especially. We get so caught up in things like data and reports that we forget what it's like to wonder like a child. So, tap into your inner 3rd grader and let your intelligence have some fun!

Action Item: Go buy a coloring book and some markers, pencils, or crayons and relive kindergarten.

TODAY:_____ _____ _____

I LOVE BECAUSE:

_____
_____
_____
_____
_____
_____
_____
_____
_____
_____
_____
_____
_____
_____
_____
_____
_____
_____
_____
_____
_____
_____
_____

Made in the USA
Columbia, SC
06 March 2019